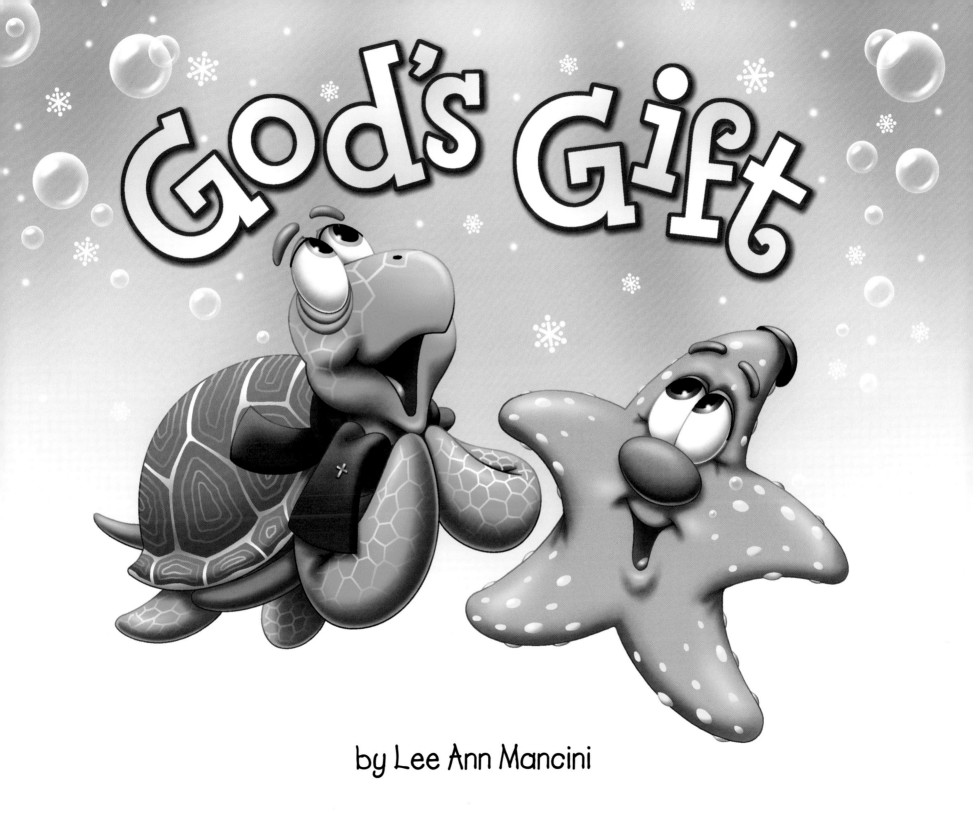

God's Gift

by Lee Ann Mancini

GLM Publishing
P.O. Box 812633
Boca Raton, Florida 33481-2633

GLMPublishing.net
SeaKidsAdventures.com

Manufactured in the USA - Printed by HCI, Inc.

Editor: Sharon Lamson

Library of Congress Control Number
2016903053

"Arise, shine, for your light has come, and the glory of the Lord rises upon you." Isaiah 60:1 (NIV)

To our beloved doggy, Princess, who was the very best Christmas present under our tree. We are thankful for all of God's gifts!

The water was chilly in the coralhood that December day.

The sea kids were having fun
helping their parents decorate the outside of their caves for the holiday season.

Christian helped his father put the Christmas lights on the huge tree in their front yard.

"Daddy, can I put Baby Jesus in the manger?" asked Christian.

"Yes, son, I think you are big enough to place Baby Jesus in the manger," replied his father.

"Wow, Daddy, thank you! I'll be careful because I know Baby Jesus is very special!"

Down the street, Jacob helped his father get ready for Hanukkah. Their house had a giant menorah outside that had three candles lit.

Jacob asked his father, "Daddy, can I light the next candle?"

"Yes, Jacob, I think you are big enough to light the next candle," answered his father.

"Why do some caves have Christmas trees and other caves have menorahs?" Jacob asked.

"Well, some families celebrate Christmas, and some celebrate Hanukkah," replied his father.

That night, Christian prayed, "Dear God, can I have a new, yellow bulldozer for Christmas? And thank you for my mommy, daddy, and my little sister. Amen."

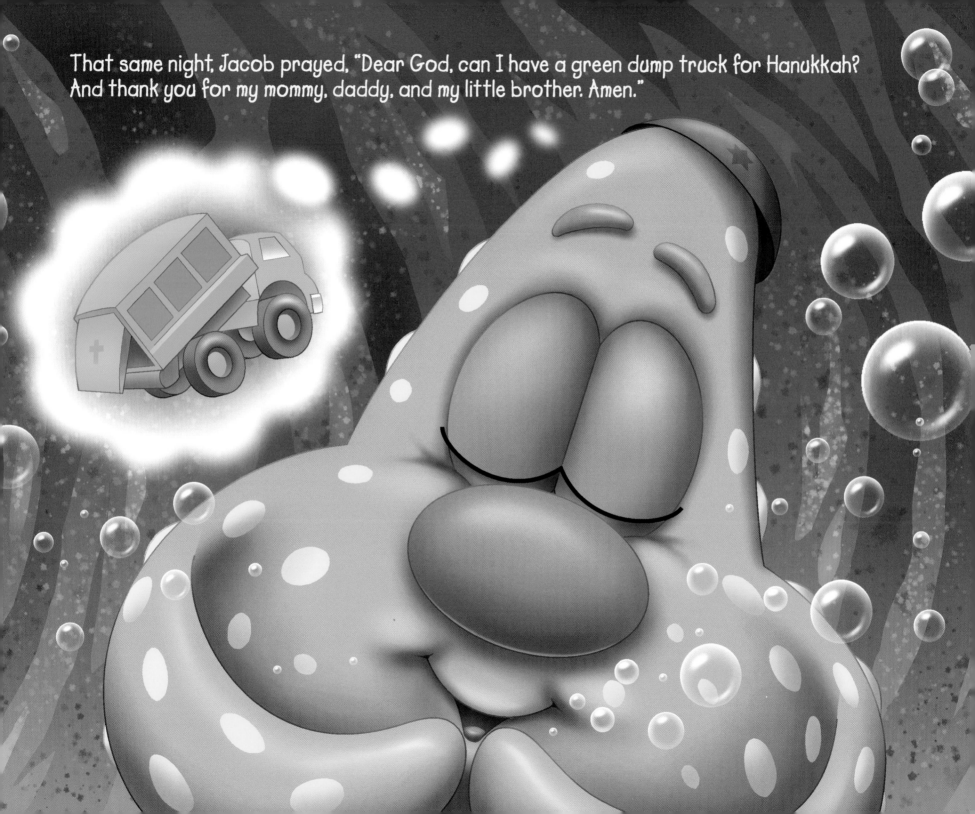

That same night, Jacob prayed, "Dear God, can I have a green dump truck for Hanukkah? And thank you for my mommy, daddy, and my little brother. Amen."

The next day, Christian and his little sister, Mary, raced out their cave door and swam to the coralhood playground.

Jacob and his little brother, Jeremiah, also raced out their cave door and swam to the coralhood playground.

The playground was full of sea kids. Some were swinging on the swings. Others were taking turns on the teeter-totter, and some were sliding down the huge octopus slide.

Some of the sea kids were gathering around Christian and Jacob, who were arguing.

"I get more toys than you because I celebrate Christmas," said Christian as he glared at Jacob. "Under our tree we get tons of presents. Christmas is way better!" Christian shouted.

"I get more toys than you because I celebrate Hanukkah," said Jacob as he glared at Christian. "We get a present every single night for eight whole days. Hanukkah is better!" Jacob shouted back.

Just then, the playground guard came over and said, "It's starting to get dark. It's time for everyone to go home."

Christian and Mary burst through their cave door and found their parents in the kitchen.

"Jacob said they get more presents at Hanukkah than we do at Christmas!" exclaimed Christian.

"It makes me sad," said Mary. "I want more presents."

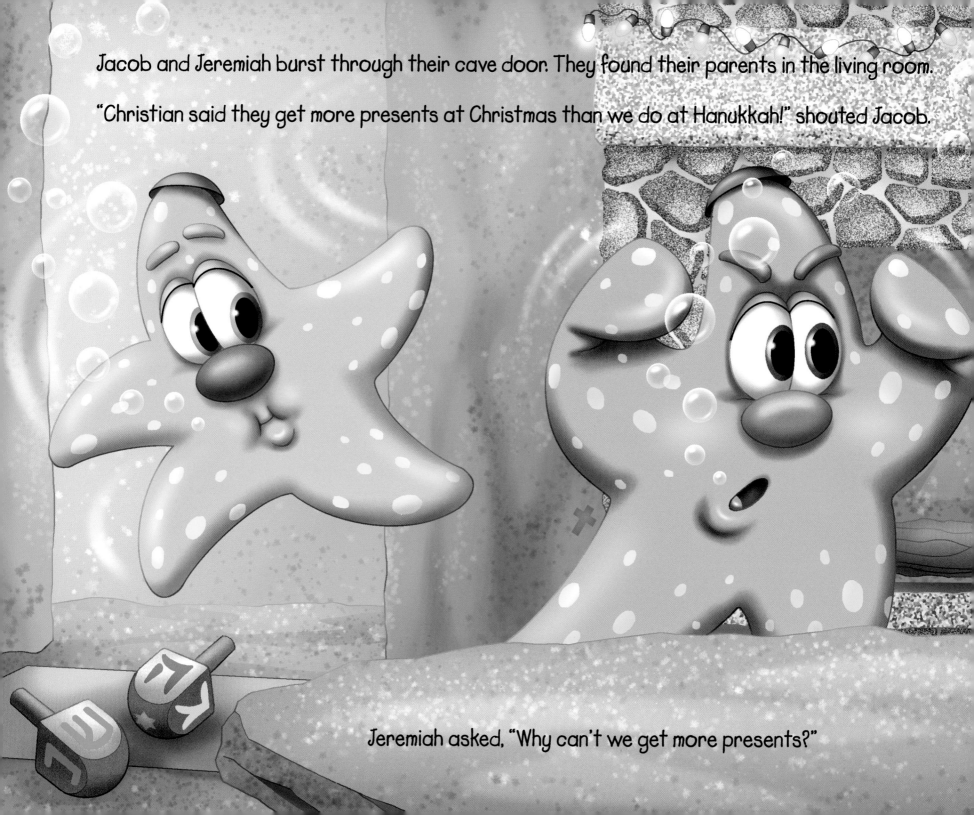

Jacob and Jeremiah burst through their cave door. They found their parents in the living room.

"Christian said they get more presents at Christmas than we do at Hanukkah!" shouted Jacob.

Jeremiah asked, "Why can't we get more presents?"

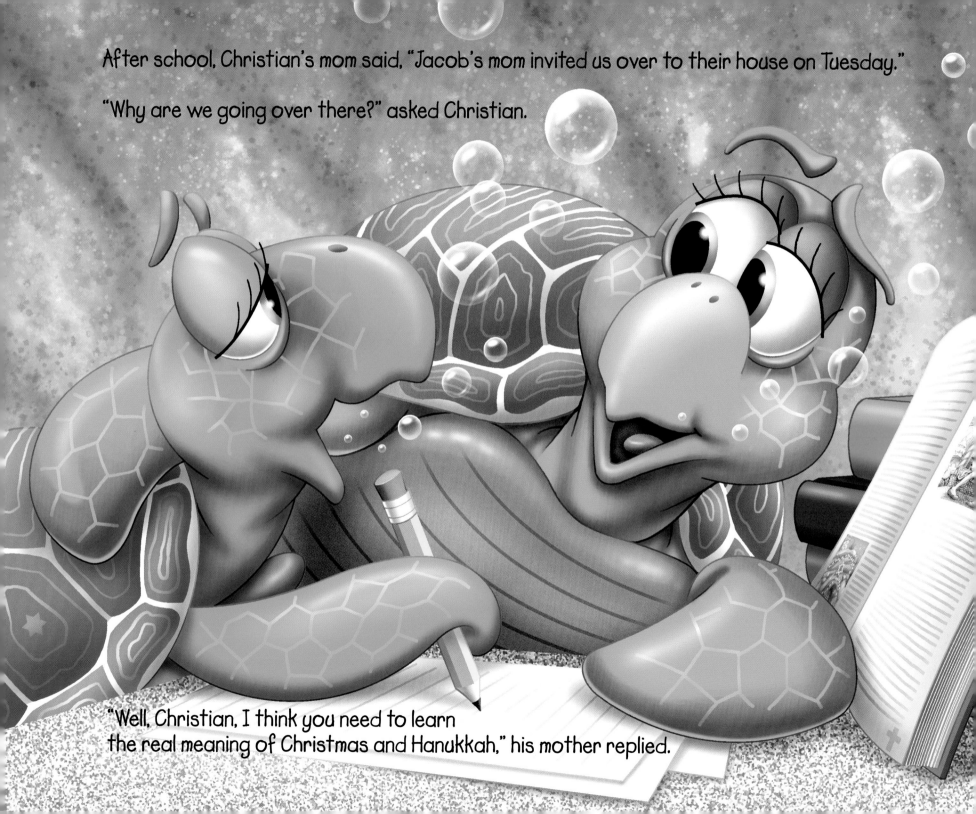

After school, Christian's mom said, "Jacob's mom invited us over to their house on Tuesday."

"Why are we going over there?" asked Christian.

"Well, Christian, I think you need to learn
the real meaning of Christmas and Hanukkah," his mother replied.

After school, Jacob's mom said, "Christian's mom invited us over to their house on Wednesday."

"Why are we going over there?" Jacob asked.

"It's not about how many toys you get, son. You and Christian should learn the true meaning of Hanukkah and Christmas," replied his mother.

When Christian arrived at Jacob's house, he saw the beautiful blue and white lights. Jewish stars hung from the ceiling. On the center of the table was a menorah with six electric candles lit brightly.

Jacob said, "Christian, I learned that Hanukkah isn't about the presents. A long time ago, there was only enough oil in the lamp for one night, but the oil lasted for eight days! God gave us the miracle of light!"

"Wow! I didn't know that," said Christian. "That's cool!"

When Jacob went to Christian's house, he saw the wonderful Christmas decorations on the tree. Underneath the tree was a beautiful manger and Baby Jesus.

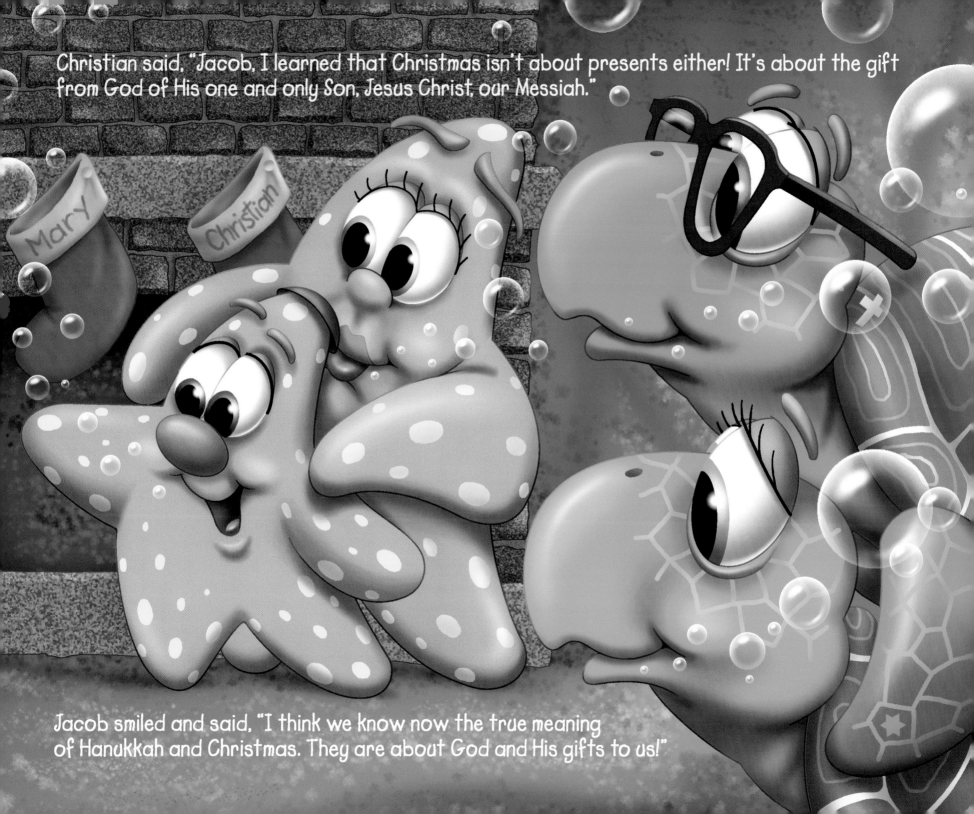

The next day, Christian and Jacob played on the playground with all their friends.

They both were looking forward to opening their gifts, but they knew in their hearts the best gift was the gift of God loving them and always taking care of them.

That night, Christian prayed, "Dear God, thank you for loving me and for the special gift of Baby Jesus. Thank you for Mommy, Daddy, all my family and all my friends. Amen!"

Jacob also prayed, "Dear God, thank you for loving me and for the gift of enough oil for eight days. Thank you for Mommy, Daddy, all my family and all my friends. Amen!"

Christmas and Hanukkah are about celebrating the gift God has given to His children. It's not about how many presents are under the tree at Christmas or the many gifts for Hanukkah. God provides for those He loves. We should always love each other as God loves us. And we should love each other for our differences!

Remember, kids, to say your prayers and always have God in your heart.
Have fun looking for the ✝ & ✡ hidden in the pictures!

GLM Publishing
GLMpublishing.net

Author: Lee Ann Mancini

Lee Ann holds a Bachelor of Religious Studies from Regent University, a Master of Biblical and Theological Studies from Knox Theological Seminary, and a Master of Christian Studies from Trinity Evangelical Divinity School. She is an Adjunct Professor at South Florida Bible College and Theological Seminary, and she serves as a board member of the Alexandrian Forum. Lee Ann is a wife and mother of two who has devoted her life as a servant for Christ.

Illustrator: Dan Sharp

Dan is an artist with over thirty years experience illustrating for children. He holds a Bachelor of Fine Arts degree from Michigan State University and has illustrated many children's books. He has specialized in the creation of licensed artwork designs for Disney, Warner Brothers, American Greetings and many other licensors of popular character properties as well. Dan loves the Lord and attends Calvary Church in Grand Rapids, Michigan.

...and many more awards!

Award-Winning Christian Book Series!

View the entire *Adventures of the Sea Kids* series at
GLMpublishing.net